THREE STOREYS UP

First published in 1997 by
Marino Books
16 Hume Street Dublin 2
An imprint of Mercier Press
Trade enquiries to CMD Distribution
55A Spruce Avenue Stillorgan Industrial
Park Blackrock County Dublin

Published in the U.S. and Canada by
the Irish American Book Company,
6309 Monarch Park Place, Niwot,
Colorado, 80503.
Telephone (303) 530-1352, (800) 452-7115.
Fax (303) 530-4488, (800) 401-9705.

Fred Kennedy 1997

ISBN 1 86023 061 X

10 9 8 7 6 5 4 3 2 1

A CIP record for this title is available
from the British Library

Cover design by Penhouse Design
Set by Richard Parfrey
Printed in Ireland by ColourBooks,
Baldoyle Industrial Estate, Dublin 13

THREE STOREYS UP

TALES OF DUBLIN TENEMENT LIFE

FRED KENNEDY

To my wife Anne, for her patience

CONTENTS

CONTENTS

1

THREE STOREYS UP

I was nine years of age when the 1939 war broke out. I was an only child and lived with my parents in a single room in a tenement house. Our room was situated three storeys up. We ate, slept and worked in one room which was sparsely furnished, consisting only of a sideboard, where we placed a few ornaments, and a wireless which ran on a dry and wet battery. We had no use for a wardrobe as all our clothing hung on nails behind the door. A heavy blanket divided our two beds but we did have a table and four chairs. A picture of Michael Collins hung on one wall and, opposite, a picture of de Valera, eyeballing each other.

My father was a small stocky man in his forties who always wanted his own way and was apt to lose his temper and shout, believing that the only way was for others to fall in with his opinions. My mother, also in her forties, was on the other hand a restrained type of person but always a match for Da when in came to arguments. For instance, Da never used that four-letter word that rhymed with 'duck'; if he did not like a person or disagreed with anyone he would tell them to 'duck off' but Ma told him he wasn't fooling the Man Above.

'Look, Jack,' she used to say, 'the Man Above knows full well when you say "duck" you really mean . . . '

'Stop where you are, woman, and remember there's a child listening with his gob open.' Ma just gave him a dirty look as she removed the blanket that separated our two beds.

The man who shared the same landing was in his fifties and like Da he was unemployed. His name was Phil, a very educated man and a bit of a philosopher, I suppose. He was a bachelor. In the hall flat lived a woman with a strange name, I always thought, for a prostitute: Lily White. Lily and Da disliked each other and she was not afraid to show her dislike whenever they met. In the room below us lived a bully of a man who was never sober, and thumped his wife every time he had drink on him and always wanted to fight every man in the house. His name was Bailey but his wife had other names for him. Three other families lived in back rooms and all ten families used two toilets which were in the yard.

These toilets were a disgrace. Broken hinges made closing the doors nearly impossible and the roofs leaked. Lily always took an umbrella when she had to sit down. As I explained before, the toilet doors only closed halfway, so that you had to keep your feet against them when you heard someone coming; some people were short on legs, so they had to whistle or cough. Poor Da, he never could whistle so he rattled a paper. Sometimes it worked and sometimes he would find himself staring into some oul' wan's face. There was always a time, especially at night, when whistles and coughing had no effect; like the time Mr Bailey rushed into the yard after a night's drinking and poor Phil was having a sit-down when he got the contents of Bailey's kidneys full in the face. Phil yelled out but Bailey only laughed. 'You want to whistle a bit louder or you'll get the contents of me bowels next time.'

Since we were three storeys up and the toilets down in the yard everyone kept clear of medicines – everyone, that is, except Da. Against Ma's advice he took a dose of Glauber's Salts. Now that was a mistake: he forgot the journey he'd have when the dose started working, three landings down and no second trousers if he had an accident. Da could have been in real trouble.

He was drinking a cup of tea when the salts erupted; he jumped up and bolted through the door but he only got as far as the first landing when he suddenly stopped; crossed his legs and twisting from one leg to the other, he slowly moved downwards. It was very important that he keep a tight cheek, if you know what I mean; otherwise there would have been a disaster. His whole body was twisted as he made his way to the second flight of stairs where he met an old lady on her way up. She wouldn't move aside and Da couldn't uncross his legs. The sweat poured from his head and the old woman seeing his twisted body moved aside.

'God bless us and save us, Mr Doyle. Did you have a stroke or something?'

'If you don't get out of me bleedin' way you'll soon find out what I have!'

Dad was a little annoyed and the old woman wasn't too pleased either at the way Da shouted at her. The only thing on Dad's mind now was: would he get an empty toilet? He did and after relieving himself he bounded up the stairs where he met the old woman again. She looked amazed as he ran past her.

'You got rid of your stroke bloody quick,' she shouted after him.

'Yeah! I left it in the toilet,' Da roared back. Needless to say, he never took Glauber's Salts again.

Three days later as Ma, Da and Phil were having a cup of tea they heard the sound of heavy hobnailed boots on the stairs below. They rushed out on to the landing and peered over the banisters. Bailey was on his way up and marking each step by banging his foot on it. He was maggoty drunk and carrying a bottle in his hand. Halfway up he decided to sit down and began singing 'Galway Bay'. Then he suddenly stopped, looked up and began to shout: 'I hope me bacon and cabbage is ready, Mary, and I hope you didn't pawn me good blue serge, like you did last week when you thought I was too drunk to notice.' He continued to sing as he staggered up the stairs. 'I'm nearly there, Mary, but I can't get the smell of me bacon and cabbage, and if it's not on the table when I walk in I'll bury this bottle in your fuckin' head.'

When he finally pushed open the door he found no Mary, no dinner and no blue serge, and he began to wreck the room. Ma, Da and Phil moved back from the banisters out of sight as Bailey emerged from his room rolling up his sleeves.

'I'll take on any man or woman in this house,' he shouted. 'If anyone wants to have a go then I'm your man!' He looked up. 'What about you, Doyle, up there in the crow's-nest or the weasel beside you?' Seeing there were no takers, he returned to his room muttering.

'I would have taken him only you held me back, Grace.' Da was brave.

'I didn't hold you back, Jack; no one even tried.'

'You wouldn't stand a chance, Jack,' Phil said. 'Did you see the size of his hands? They were like two shovels.'

'I don't know so much about that, Phil. I'm fairly fast on me feet.' Da started to demonstrate his boxing pose. 'I would have dazzled him with me footwork alone.'

'And if he planted his hobnails between your legs you wouldn't be doin' much dancin',' said Ma.

Da changed the subject. 'By the way, Grace, where did Mary Bailey disappear to?'

'She's gone to live with her sister in Liverpool. She told me in confidence that she was goin' to pawn his blue serge and buy a one-way ticket to Liverpool.'

'She should have done that a long time ago,' Phil said. The next day the landlord had Bailey arrested and he wasn't seen again.

I remember the first time I heard Da using the word 'duck'. It was two o'clock in the morning when I woke up bursting to go to the toilet. I knew I'd never make it. 'Da!' I cried out three times.

'What's wrong with you?' he shouted

'I want to go to the toilet but the po is full.' Well it would be with three on it.

'Open the window and throw it out,' he replied angrily.

'There might be some people underneath, Da.'

'Then they'll think it's raining, won't they?'

'And if they're looking up . . . '

'Then they'll know it's not rainin'. Just duck it out and go back to sleep.'

'What do you mean, 'duck' it out?'

'He means: fuck it out,' Ma screamed. 'Now go back to sleep.'

'That's lovely language at two in the mornin' and in front of the child. Is it any wonder I can't get a job; you should wash out that mouth of yours!'

'Ah, wash me arse!'

Da was mad. 'Here I am, praying to St Joseph to be on the lookout for a job and the only thing you want me to do is wash your arse.'

'I didn't think St Joseph was lookin' for a job but if he can't get one Christ help *you*!' Ma was being sarcastic. 'By the way, Charlie, did you empty that po yet?'

I threw the contents of the po out of the window; all hell broke out. A woman screamed and Ma went to the window.

'Is there something the matter down there?' she asked.

'You dirty bitch!' a young woman's voice shouted up, 'you've just drowned me and me boyfriend with piss.'

'Isn't that a shame!' Ma shouted down. 'Well, if yis weren't interferin' with one another . . . '

'We're doin' nothin' wrong, you interferin' oul' bitch.'

'Yis must be doin' it right because you're after frightenin' me cat.' I didn't know we had a cat. 'Why don't you go and stand in front of the oul' wan's window and do what you're tryin' to do under mine.'

Da got out of bed and pushed Ma away from the window.

'Do you have to make a show of yourself, Grace! It's

none of your business what that couple are doin', whether they're doin' it the right way or the wrong way. Anyway she'll know soon enough if they did it the right way.'

'It's gettin' now that a body can't empty their own po without someone shoutin' blue murder,' said Ma.

2

WHAT DID YOU DO IN THE WAR, DA?

I was starting my school holidays when the German army invaded France and Da didn't like that one little bit. We had just finished breakfast when Phil walked in.

'Did you hear the latest news, Phil?'

'What news was that, Jack?'

'The Germans are walking through France and rounding up all the Jews and marchin' them straight into the gas chambers.' Da banged his fist on the table in anger. 'They'll be over here next, you mark my words.'

'They'll have to take England first before they take us on, Jack.'

Da stood up from the table, very annoyed. 'They'll go through England like a dose of salts.' Ma started to laugh; Da didn't like that. 'It's no laughing matter, Grace. Don't forget: half a dozen bombs on Dublin and the city would be oblit . . . oblit . . . '

'Obliterated is the word, Jack,' Phil enlightened him. 'I don't think the Germans would be bothered with us.'

'Phil is right, Jack. There's not enough Jews in the country to bother them.'

Da walked up and down the room shaking his head. 'It's not only Jews they're after, woman, but the whole of Europe. Hitler is a lunatic and someone has got to stop him.'

'What do you propose, Jack?' asked Phil with a slight smirk.

'I don't know what *you* are goin' to do but I'm goin' to join up. I'm not goin' to sit on me arse and let this madman take over the country. Do yis realise, both of yis, that this man could be takin' the salute in O'Connell Street on St Patrick's Day?'

Ma walked to the window and stared out for a second; then turned to Da. 'My dear husband,' she said in a gentle voice, 'you're too old for the army and besides, what do you know about modern warfare? I can just picture you on the first day you came face to face with a German.' She began to laugh. 'You wouldn't be long running home if he stuck his bayonet up your arse.'

Da wasn't amused but he didn't look too upset. 'Who said anything about the army? I'll enlist in the local defence force.' Phil sitting on the edge of the bed looked seriously at Da. 'Your wife is right, Jack. You've got to be tough and know how to handle firearms and ... '

'The local defence can help the regular army with some of their duties.'

'Like what?' Ma asked.

Da looked awkward. 'Keeping a lookout for German paratroopers,' he informed her, 'and watching the docks and patrolling all other waterways. There's a lot we can do, anyway. I'm off the first thing in the morning to Portobello barracks to sign up.'

Ma started to cough loudly. 'What's the hurry, Jack?' she said, trying to stifle a smile. 'The Germans won't be coming for another year or two, and there's another thing you should know . . . '

'An' what's that, may I ask?'

'You'll have to pass a medical.'

Da stood up from the table and began to expand his chest. 'There's nothin' the matter with me; I'll have no bother passin' . . . '

'Piss,' Phil muttered.

Da gave him a dirty look. 'What did you just say?'

'You'll have to give a urine sample.' Da looked puzzled. 'What will they do . . . I mean . . . What will I have to do?'

'Piss into the bottle. That tells them a lot about your condition, and also a blood test. It's a very rigorous examination, Jack.'

Da looked over at Ma, then back at Phil. 'Does everyone have to give a urine test?' he wanted to know.

'Yes,' Ma said, 'especially if you're sent to the front lines.'

'And what am I supposed to do when I get to the front lines? Piss on the Germans? I can't understand all this shit. Here we have the German army a couple of hundred miles away and all this government wants to know is: did you piss in the bottle before you left? The Germans will love that.'

'We can always stick lemonade labels on the bottles and sell it to the Germans; that should get rid of them.'

Da turned away from the window and gave Phil a dirty look; then he rubbed his hands together. 'This time tomorrow I'll be in the defence force and if they want me to piss in a bottle then I'll piss in a bottle; I'll even piss on the floor if they want me to. But I'll be a part-time soldier this time tomorrow.'

Da was true to his word. He did join the local defence force and arrived in his uniform. I was very proud of him that day: John Wayne in a brown habit. But Ma didn't think so. She put her hands to her face when he marched into the room. 'Sacred Heart of Jesus,' she cried out. 'That uniform . . . its like the brown habit me father was buried in, same make, same colour.'

Da ignored her; he was happy. 'I think it's a nice shade of brown.' He then removed his cap which was shaped just like a boat. 'The hat goes well with the uniform, don't you think, Grace?'

Ma was furious. 'You can go to Mass on Sunday on your own. I wouldn't be seen walkin' with you in that rag.'

'What the duckin' hell is wrong with it? I'm proud to be wearin' it so you can get stuffed.'

He stood up straight and marched up and down in front of the picture of Michael Collins and saluted. All three of us exchanged glances. 'Are we ready for the fray now, Jack?' Ma asked sarcastically. 'Watching the airports and the waterways.'

'Yes, and I'll be home late; so don't wait up from me.'

'Are you taking a flask with you?' Phil asked.

'Don't be so duckin' funny.' Da looked across at me and then at Ma. 'I'll see you both later.' Then he left.

The next morning the stillness of the day was shattered by Lily White's voice. 'Are you up there, Jacko?' she shouted. Da attempted to get up from the table but Ma told him to ignore her. 'I saw you last night patrolling the canal with your baton in your hand. Was it submarines you were after or a good woman?' Da and Ma jumped up together. I was pushed to one side as they rushed on to the landing.

Ma held on to the banisters and shouted down. 'Go an' wash yourself, you dirty brasser!'

Lily didn't like that. 'I'm no brasser, I'll have you know. I'm a respectable woman, a business woman. I give a service, and without me and a good many others, you and your kind wouldn't be safe walking the streets at night. Put that in your baton and bash it, Jack.'

'I'll be waiting on your next client to come along,' Da warned her. 'And when he does arrive I'll have a nice surprise for him.' I could hardly wait to find out what the surprise was.

Lily only laughed. 'My clients, as you call them, are all gentlemen and nothing in this kip would surprise them.'

'A bucket of shite on top of the head should shake them up a bit!' So that was the surprise!

Da was in great form after that but Phil then joined them on the balcony. 'Will you two get back inside and ignore that woman!' he urged.

But Lily continued her barracking. 'Are you still there, Jacko? Just in case your intelligence officer doesn't inform you, the Germans are on their way.'

'You'll do a roaring trade when they do arrive,' Ma shouted down.

'Just picture it, ma'am. I'll have more soldiers than General Alexander.'

'I hope you don't infect this house if you get a dose of the crabs or something else.'

'It can't be as bad as the dose you married!'

That did it. Da made a wild dash for the stairs but Phil grabbed him and hauled him back.

'You're only making things worse, answering her back', Phil told him.

But Da was still mad as he struggled with him. 'She called me a dose; you heard her yourself.' He looked at Ma. 'You heard her, Grace; didn't you?'

'I did, Jack, and I'm just thinkin': wouldn't it be a good idea if you resigned from the defence force. Then she wouldn't be slaggin' you so much.'

Phil moved closer to the door. 'Grace is right, Jack. These war games are only for the young and the brave, and let's be honest, you're neither.'

Da was not a bit amused and he was disappointed that Phil and Ma should belittle him. 'You both think I'm bleedin' windy.'

'Phil doesn't mean anything like that, Jack.' Ma tried to pacify him but she was only making things worse. 'You must face facts, Jack,' she continued. 'You are not properly trained for soldiering. And remember: the only weapon you have is a baton to defend yourself – and besides you'll only make a holy show of us all.' The very minute Ma began to ridicule Da I grabbed the bedpost and held on grimly. Da picked up his baton and made a wild charge towards Ma but Phil flung his arms round him and pushed him into a chair.

'You're a silly man and your wife is only speaking the truth. You are ill-prepared both mentally and physically, especially the first bit.'

This did not help one little bit. I could see Da was

about to explode from the way he was clenching and unclenching his fist. It was always a sign.

'Do yis both think I'm a bleedin' tulip and not able to defend my family in this hour of darkness . . . Is that what you're thinkin'?'

Ma sat down, resigned to the fact that she was on a loser but she made no effort to console him. The trouble is she made things worse.

'Jack,' she said. 'We know your intentions are good but let's face it . . . suppose the Germans came marching down the road, what could you do? Shag all – and you know it!'

'And I'm supposed to let them walk all over me without a struggle? Is that what you'd like me to do?'

Ma then came up with a beauty. 'There doesn't have to be a struggle, Jack, and there won't be a struggle . . . '

'How do you make that out?' Da was curious – and puzzled.

'Well, first of all the German officer would simply walk up to you and order you to hand over your baton. He would then take that baton and proceed to knock your fuckin' brains out, which would not be too difficult.'

Da made a mad rush towards Ma, pushing Phil out of the way, but the sound of Lily's voice stopped him in his tracks.

'Are you up there, General,' she mocked. 'The man on the wireless said that the Germans have landed in Dún Laoghaire and I'll be out there to greet them.'

Da leapt to the banisters. 'You don't have to wait for the Germans to come and flog your mutton; you've already got your own army.' Lily gave a hearty laugh and rushed back into her room. Da was fuming. 'I'll swing for that hoor's melt yet.'

Phil smiled and put his arm round him. 'I've got a drop of the hard stuff in me room. Come in and join me.' They both left. The war finally ended, although it was years later when I found out. The Germans didn't even know where Dún Laoghaire was.

3

UNHAPPY MEDIUM

I clearly remember an experience I had during the last year of the war. I had just arrived home from school and found Ma rushing and fussing around the room. She told me to finish my dinner quickly as she wanted the table.

'What for?' I asked curiously.

'There's a woman coming round about six o'clock . . .'

I was a little puzzled and interjected, 'Are we selling the table, Ma?' She laughed but did explain.

The lady expected was a medium; that's someone who talks to the spirit world. Ma was about to tell me more when Da arrived, and by the look on his face *he* had found some spirits. Ma explained to him about the coming of the medium but he just stared at her.

'What time is this oul' wan coming?'

'About six or so, and I just wanted to get everything ready. I'm so excited.'

'Whose idea was this? I mean . . . Christ only knows what this medium is goin' to bring into the house. Anyway, who are we waitin' for?'

'Mrs Farrell is hoping to contact the spirit of her late

husband Sam, although for the life of me I don't know why. He wasn't much good when he was alive.'

Da sat down and then said something he should never have said. 'I hope she doesn't bring your mother back by mistake.' Ma picked up a plate and crashed it against the wall just as Phil entered.

'Did I miss anything?'

'The only thing I missed was that gobshite of a husband of mine.' Ma continued on with her cleaning and explained the forthcoming visit of a certain mystic.

Phil didn't believe in that sort of nonsense; to him spirits only came in bottles. 'When you're gone you're gone, and there's no coming back.'

'I agree with Phil,' Da said; then turned to Ma. 'Why is this shaggin' thing being held here? Why not a pub or oul' Farrell's place?'

Ma stopped sweeping the floor and sat down. 'I'll tell you why, and it seems silly: she simply doesn't want her late husband to know she's still living in the same kip.'

'So she moved from one kip to another,' Phil murmured.

Da heard him. 'Hold on a minute, Phil. This might be a kip but it's a clean kip.'

Ma continued to fuss about and eventually joined them at the table. 'You know, Phil, I never really liked the man when he was alive. I always thought he was a bit of a slither.'

Phil nodded his head and turned to Da. 'I thought he was a bit queer myself. What did you think of him, Jack?'

Da thought for a minute or two. 'Well, Phil, he didn't strike me as a straight man, if you know what I mean – more like . . . '

'He was a little bent; is that what you mean, Jack?'

'We'll soon find out which way he walks . . . if he ever arrives,' Ma said with a wry smile.

At six o'clock on the dot the medium arrived. She was a tall, lean and forbidding-looking person with a face like a well-smacked arse. An eerie feeling crept over me. Was I going to see spirits flying around the room? I hoped not. Mrs Farrell was a buxom woman and wore glasses, and like the medium was in her sixties. She introduced her to the family. 'Mrs Daly, this is Mr Doyle and his wife.'

Da pointed to Phil. 'And this man is a good friend of the family. He stays next door.'

'This lady will endeavour to contact the spirit of me late husband Sam,' Mrs Farrell informed them. 'I have an uneasy feeling that poor Sam is unhappy and not at ease.' She turned to the medium. 'Whenever you're ready . . . '

Mrs Daly moved across and sat at the table. She took out a candle from her bag and instructed Ma to close the curtains; semi-darkness was what she needed. She then lit the candle and told them to gather round the table and hold hands. I was confined to the farthest corner of the room. The flickering candle sent all sorts of shapes on to the ceiling. The silence was deadly for a minute or two but when I saw Da move sideways I knew that silence was about to be shattered. The fart could be heard in the next street. Mrs Daly took her hanky out of her bag and coughed into it. Ma looked angry and glared at Da.

'Will you for once show a little respect and cork that gas-hole,' she shouted across the table.

Da only smiled. 'There's many a man in Glasnevin cemetery today who'd be glad to release some of that gas.'

Phil looked uncomfortable as he turned to Da. 'This is not the place to be blowin' off, Jack; this is serious business here. I'd like to know what exactly is going to happen.'

Mrs Farrell was angry and the medium wasn't too happy either as she turned to her. 'If you want me to contact your husband's spirit I must have complete silence. I feel he's quite near and anxious to get in touch with his loved one.' There was a slight titter round the table. Farrell glared at Ma, then Da. She even turned her stare on me. Phil looked uneasy and Ma noticed.

'Is something the matter, Phil?'

'It might be my imagination but I felt a minute ago something cold on me thigh ... like a hand.'

He looked nervously at Mrs Farrell who gave him a fierce look. 'What are you lookin' at me for? You don't think for a minute that I'm interferin' with your person, the bloody cheek of you anyway.'

'I didn't say you were, Mrs Farrell. I only thought that your husband's spirit might have had something to do with it ... but I did feel something cold and damp.'

Farrell started to laugh. 'Maybe you wet yourself?'

Da was getting fidgety and that was bad. 'This whole thing is gettin' out of hand and the only spirit in this house is in a baby bottle. If someone has one in their bag, then they should release it now.'

Mrs Daly was mad and started to stare into space. Then she looked at Farrell. 'Your late husband was about to contact me but he's gone now. I think he's a little unhappy this moment.'

'And who can blame him, the poor soul?' Farrell

glanced round her but Da wasn't having any more.

'Well,' he said, 'we may as well pack up and, as Phil says, when you're dead you're bleedin' dead and that's about that.'

Mrs Daly was not amused: 'Are you insinuatin', Mr Doyle, that I'm not capable of delving into the spirit word?'

'Excuse me, Mrs Daly, but I don't think Sam Farrell's spirit wants to come back ... He thought he'd never get away in the first place.'

Farrell reacted angrily to Da's outburst. 'What's a gobshite like you know about the spirit world! You're as stupid and mean as the remainder of your clan.'

Ma then got on her bike. 'The biggest gobshite of all was your own late husband, and you were not far behind as regards meanness. You didn't think much of him when you started to traipse around looking for the cheapest habit you could find. You got one from the nuns and the poor undertaker, God love him, nearly died himself when the bloody cheap habit burst open and the man's skidoo popped out for everyone to see.'

That did it. Farrell was livid and who could blame her? 'You can say what you like, Doyle, but at least he was a man and not like the yoke you married.'

'Oh he was a man all right; everyone in the street knew that, the moment he stood buck-naked in front of the window and him playin' his mouth-organ at the same time.'

Farrell with a wan smile stood up from the table. 'He could knock out a tune or two out of that oul' mouth-organ ... '

'He knocked a tune out of a lot with his instrument when he was alive . . . '

'You have a big mouth, Doyle, and you know what they say about a woman with a big mouth, don't yeh?'

I didn't know what they said about a woman with a big mouth but Ma did. 'Didn't your late husband knock the bejasus out of yeh twice a week, what are yeh talking about!' Farrell was really angry now as she reached across the table and grabbed Ma by the hair, sending chairs flying all over the room. Both women were scratching and clawing at each other as they rolled around the room. Farrell's glasses flew off her nose and landed at my feet. I snatched them up and jumped back on the bed.

Ma was winning because she was on top but as they continued to struggle, Farrell's clothes went over her head and she had no underwear. Poor Phil never saw a sight like it in his life. His jaw dropped, his eyes bulged out of their sockets and for a minute I thought he had gone into a coma. At this point Da decided to intervene and began to pull the women apart, pushing Ma on to my bed and marshalling Farrell towards the door. After brushing herself down she picked up her handbag from the floor and turning round she gave Da a belt across the face. Then turning to leave she walked into the wall. I ran across and handed her the glasses back, while Da opened the door. 'Off you go, Mrs Farrell, and don't ever come back.' She flew downstairs.

Meanwhile Mrs Daly, who had been quiet throughout, moved towards the door. 'I'm sure Sam Farrell's spirit is breaking his shite laughing at the lot of you. Is it any wonder he decided to stay put.' These were the last words the medium spoke as she raced down the stairs. Ma began to straighten the room, while Da rearranged the chairs in their proper places. All three sat down and had a good laugh but the laughter soon stopped when Da put his finger to his lips and looked scared.

'What is it, Jack?' Ma's voice trembled.

'The stairs. I thought I heard a creaking noise, like someone sneaking up.'

'Those stairs have been creaking for the past fifty years, Jack.'

Da held his hands up. 'Keep quiet for a moment, Phil ... I'm sure I heard something.' We all kept quiet, especially me. No one dared breathe. Suddenly we heard the distinct sound of footsteps being trod lightly on the stairs. Phil and Da exchanged nervous glances. Da looked across towards Ma.

'Grace, go to the door and gently open it and see if there is anyone about.'

'I will in my shite go! Why don't *you* go! After all, you were the one who was goin' to flatten the Germans.'

Poor Phil, he seemed to be in a trance; his voice was shaky as he spoke. 'I'm only going to ask one question. It may be silly but I have to ask ... '

'What is it, Phil? What's the question?'

'Spirits don't wear boots, Jack. Do they?'

'Phil, no one knows what they wear in the spirit world. They could be goin' round in their skin for all we know – that would suit Sam!'

'For Christ's sake Sam Farrell hadn't a shoe on his feet when he was alive; so it can't be him,' Ma said as she poured herself a cup of cold tea.

The footsteps stopped suddenly outside the door. Phil flattened himself against the wall. Ma's hand began to shake, spilling some of her tea over Da, who seemed stuck to the chair.

'Jack, go and see who it is and ask them what they want,' Ma whispered.

'I can't, Grace, me bowels are beginning to move and it might be dangerous if I left the chair.'

A loud knock seemed to echo round the room. Ma dropped her cup, Phil looked dead standing up and Da fell off the chair but quickly picked himself up and moved cautiously to the door. 'I don't know who you are there, but if it's money you're after you won't find a bleedin' deuce in this house. So duck off!'

'It's only me, Mr Doyle – the medium ... Remember me?'

'What do you want now?'

'I left without me candle. It's a special candle blessed by the Pope himself.'

Da pushed the candle through the slightly open door. 'Here's your special candle, Mrs Daly, and I hope the Pope had better luck than you had,' he said, as he banged the door shut and rejoined Phil and Ma at the table.

Phil reached into his back pocket and drew out a naggin of brandy. 'Would you two people care to partake in a little spirit with me?' I turned on my side and went to sleep.

4

HEAVEN HELP THE WORKING MAN

Although the war had ended we still had to hold on to our ration-books and the glimmerman was still sniffing around to make sure we were using gas only when we should. Still we got a bit of good news: the labour exchange sent Da after a job. It was as a nightwatchman in a builder's yard in a tough part of the city. He brought me along to collect cards and the clerk behind the brass grill was delighted for him.

'How long have you been with us, Jack?'

'Since yis opened – at least it seems that long. I'd say . . . about ten years. And I must say I got great service in that time.'

'Thursday won't be the same without you; anyway, good luck!'

Da started the next day and Mr Martin, his boss, came to see him and introduced himself. 'I'm Mr Martin, your boss, and I want to warn you to be vigilant at all times. This area is full of thieves and is well known to the police.'

'Don't you worry, Mr Martin. No one will get past me, rest assured.'

Da was brave and for the next few weeks he seemed to enjoy his post. However, the night work was to be his downfall. One evening, feeling under the weather, he climbed to the top of a bulldozer – just to look around, mind you – and fell asleep. When he finally woke up he discovered that ten bags of cement and a fifteen-foot girder were missing. He rushed out, looked left and right but there was no sign of life. That morning when his boss arrived the first thing he noticed was a missing girder. He took his cap off and scratched his head. When he found out about the missing cement he screamed at Da.

'What happened here last night, Doyle, and where were you when it was happening? A girder and ten bags of cement! What sort of a fuckin' watchman are you!'

'I'm sorry, Mr Martin . . . ' Then he began to lie. 'I thought I heard someone trying to break in at the back gate so I climbed on top of the bulldozer for a better look, and . . . I must have dozed off.'

'Oh is that all? Well, while you were nodding off ten bags and a fifteen foot girder were nodding off down the road, and they would have taken the bleedin' bulldozer but they were very kind and didn't want to waken you up. Now get out of me sight, and if I ever hear that you were in on this robbery I'll take your sacred life.'

Poor Da, now he had to face Ma, the ultimate test, but he was surprised when he got home. Ma wasn't too angry over him losing his job. 'Jack,' she said, 'face facts: you've lost the habit of work; you were never cut out for it and I'm sure they'll be delighted to see you back on hatch twenty-one. One thing more, the next time you meet up with St Joseph ask him if he knows where the cement and the girder ended up.'

Da ignored her sarcasm. 'I just can't understand how they got the girder out without me hearin' somethin'. I know I nodded off but I would have heard the lorry pulling out.'

'You mean they stole a lorry as well?'

Da shook his head. 'No, no. The police say they probably had a lorry on stand outside the yard.' He looked unhappy as he walked about the room. 'They won't be very happy in the labour exchange when they hear about this.'

Ma started again after she had finished making the beds. 'I wonder will they give you the same hatch as before, Jack? After all you can claim seniority; you were there when everybody else was out working.'

This was Ma at her best. 'Keep flapping those lips of yours, Grace, and you could end up on a slab.'

I was glad when Phil entered. It lifted the tension a bit – or so I thought. He looked nervously at Da and his voice was a little shaky when he spoke. 'I'm sorry to hear you lost your job, Jack.'

'Who told you that?'

'I heard it down in the bookie's shop. Everyone down there has it; even Lily White knows.'

Da went livid at the mention of her name. 'She's a hoor's melt if ever there was one.'

Phil took his cap off and sat down. Ma stood with her back to the dresser with folded arms.

'What actually happened?' he asked.

'Did the queer one not tell you?'

'She said something about a girder.'

'That's right, Phil,' Ma interjected, 'and ten bags of cement.'

Phil's jaw dropped and he looked across at Da. 'I thought you were supposed to be mindin' the place.'

Ma was about to join in but she caught Da's eye. He pointed a finger at her. 'If you don't want to join your ancestors then I'd advise you to keep that mouth of yours shut.'

But Ma was defiant. 'Why don't you tell Phil the whole story?'

Phil was puzzled. 'Tell me what?'

Ma began to edge closer to the door as Da showed signs of a man about to explode. Then he cooled down, changed his mind and began to lie. 'I chased a couple of kids I thought were goin' to break in . . . '

'That's not the way I heard it, Jack.'

'And which duckin' way did you hear it?'

'Lily told everyone you fell asleep on top of a bull-dozer.'

'And how would she know?'

'Your ex-boss, Mr Martin, told her. He's a client of hers, you know, and when you were on top of the bulldozer . . .'

' . . . he was on top of her!'

'Ah, I wouldn't go that far, Jack. After all he comes from a very respectable family.'

'So did Genghis Khan.'

'Is that the racehorse owner?' Phil enquired.

Ma then wanted to show off. 'You're thinkin' of the Aga Khan; he's the one that owns the horses, Phil. Genghis is probably his father.'

Da threw his eyes to heaven and changed the subject. 'Grace, would you mind, that's if it's not too much trouble, making a drop of tea and . . . '

'Are you up there, Jacko?' Lily was back in town and the very sound of her voice drove Da crazy.

He made a dash for the door, stumbled over a chair, flung open the door and shouted down, 'I'll have the parish priest here first thing in the morning and . . . '

'You're too late, Jacko. I had him here this morning. Someone told him he'd get a bag of cement cheap, and if he hears of anyone looking for a fifteen-foot girder he'll let me know.'

Her hysterical laugh enraged Da and in the struggle to release himself from Phil's grip he stumbled down a few steps with Ma and Phil landing on top of him.

Ma quickly got to her feet, brushed herself down and glared at Da. 'I told you before not to be mindin' that village bike.'

On their way back to our room Lily started up again. 'I forgot to tell you, Jacko. Mr Martin informed the labour exchange of your little misdemeanour, which means you're a lifter. It also means no free beef voucher for the next six weeks. But don't worry: I have enough mutton down here for the three of yis.'

'Keep your infected mutton for your clients,' Ma shouted back but Lily just ignored her and banged her door shut. Ma then turned her anger on Da.

'Well Mr Doyle, what are we supposed to eat for the next six weeks? Grass?' Then her manner changed and I think she felt sorry, as she put her arms round him. 'What an exciting day this has been, Jack!'

Da with a dejected look threw his eyes heavenwards and smiled.

To me, however, it was a day like any other day . . . poxy!

5
—

SVDP

When Da's labour was stopped for six weeks due to Mr Martin reporting him for his latest escapade Ma decided to seek help from St Vincent de Paul's. She was told how a widow down the road and with no family received a bag of coal and ten shillings every week. Da was excited and prepared the room for the official's arrival.

'Are you sure the Vincent's man will be here tonight, Grace?'

'Well they told me someone would call, so we'd better be ready for them.'

'What do you mean, be ready?'

'Well first of all, let the fire die out. Then they'll know we have no firing.'

'The fire is already dead. The only thing that's burning is an old pair of slippers Phil gave us. That fire has been dead for two days.'

'All right,' Ma said as she glanced at the clock. 'They usually come around eight and it's half past seven now.' Da rushed over, picked up three empty stout bottles and rolled them under the bed.

'These people are dead cute, Grace. They know by looking around if you are entitled to anything. If they were to see empty stout bottles hanging around then it would be "Goodnight, Irene".'

Ma then started on me.

'Charlie,' she said, 'when this person arrives, if you are asked any questions always say, "Yes, sir!" and if it's a woman say, "Yes ma'am!" and "No, ma'am!" Now don't forget. And if you want a cut of bread just ask for it.' I wondered where the bread was coming from all of a sudden; we had none at teatime.

'We'll have to be very careful, Jack,' Ma warned. 'These people are no cods.'

'I believe they're very sharp all right; they can pick out a chancer in a flash. Anyway, we're ready for them and I hope nothing goes wrong.'

I was proud of Ma and Da at that moment. They had everything in its place; even the Sacred Heart lamp was lighting and that lamp hadn't been lighting for months. They were like two generals preparing for battle, every little plan laid out meticulously ... or was it?

At 8.15 there was a loud rap on the door. Ma rushed and opened it. The man outside was tall, with a moustache. He wore a long black overcoat and looked to be in his sixties.

'Mrs Doyle, my name is Walsh and I'm from St Vincent's. I believe you need a little assistance?'

'Yes, sir ... ' Ma's voice was shaky, ' ... this is my husband and son Charlie.'

He nodded his head and walked slowly round the room, writing in a little notebook. He began to mooch towards the sideboard, where he picked up an empty whiskey bottle. Ma and Da exchanged nervous glances.

'We keep that bottle for holy water, sir.' Da was smart. 'It's been in the house for years. Me mother, God rest her, kept that bottle just for the water. As a matter of fact, Charlie here was to get some holy water on his way home from school and he forgot to bring the bottle.' I didn't know that.

'I believe a drop of whiskey goes well with holy water,' the man said in a sarcastic tone.

Now it was my turn. 'Ma, I feel hungry. Can I have a cut of bread?'

'No, we have no bread in the house . . . yet.'

The Vincent man looked at Ma, then at me. 'They have you well-tutored, son,' he said with a smile. I didn't think things are working out the way the two generals thought they would, and if I'm to blame for asking for a lousy cut of bread then I'm dead. Mr Walsh gazed at the picture of Michael Collins with a wry smile on his face. Then he stared at the picture of de Valera and a look of approval appeared on his face. 'Dev was a great leader, Mr Doyle, a great man altogether.'

He should never have said that. Da turned on him. 'Then why the bleedin' hell didn't he go to London with the others.'

Ma could see the bag of coal and the bread going down the Liffey. She changed her colours and there were other changes on the way. 'You're quite right, sir; my late father was a great Dev man himself and like you say, he was a great leader.'

'Yes indeed, Mrs Doyle, and if he had gone along with

Collins we wouldn't have a border today.'

Was Da angry? Of course he was! He looked at Ma. 'Your father was a gobshite, Grace, and you, sir, you are another gobshite. I never heard such a load of bullshite in my whole life.' Da was mad and it's never a pretty sight. He stabbed his finger into Mr Walsh's chest. 'Collins was a great intelligence officer and master of disguises . . . Do you know, he once drove a coal dray past the British soldiers. They were looking for him, mind you, and they never recognised him. He carried a bag of coal on his shoulders up two flights of stairs and delivered papers at the same time. Then he walked calmly into the street shaking his empty bag under their noses, and in the end Dev's men shot him in the back.'

'That's not true . . . ' Walsh was angry now. 'Collins was shot by his own men in his own county.'

'You're a bigger gobshite than I thought you were,' Da shouted angrily.

I had an idea that St Vincent's coal would never be burning in our fireplace and by the look on Ma's face we were going to get feck all. Mr Walsh with a solemn look on his face continued to jot down a few things as we looked on in silence. He turned to Ma as he moved towards the door. 'Mrs Doyle,' he said, handing her a note, 'this will get you a quarter pound of butter, a couple of loaves of bread and five bob for the house. I'll see you next week.'

He was halfway downstairs when Da shouted, 'What about a bag of coal?'

'Ask Michael Collins to bring you one!' Walsh shouted back.

'You're bleedin' very funny,' Da roared out. Ma turned to him and showed him the food voucher. 'It's not too bad, Jack. At least we'll be able to buy a bit of meat with the five bob, and we might have got a little more if you hadn't called him a gobshite.'

At that moment Phil entered. 'Well, how did yis get on?'

'We didn't get a bag of coal anyway, Phil, but he did give us a food voucher and five bob.'

'I thought you would have got a bag of coal, Jack.'

'We would have only he had to open his big mouth.'

'Why, what did he say?'

'He called the man a gobshite.'

'That would do it.' He turned to Da. 'What made you say a thing like that for?'

'Ah, he started to talk about Collins and that Dev feller and things got a bit out of hand. And you didn't help matters when you left an empty whiskey bottle on the sideboard and right under his nose.'

'Did he cop it?'

'Of course he did. The man's a genius at his work . . . knew all the tricks.'

'Like what?' Phil was curious.

'Like people rolling empty beer bottles under the bed and strippin' wallpaper off the walls and making the place worse than it was. At least we had the altar lamp lightin'.'

'Did it help, Jack?'

'I don't think so. The minute I saw him lightin' his cigarette off the lamp I knew he had no respect for it and we were on a loser.'

'Talking about the lamp, Jack. I haven't seen it lit this

past six months. Where did you get the paraffin oil from?'

'A nightwatchman down the road was filling his lamps and he kindly gave me a drop.'

Da was a genius. What other man would think of carrying an altar lamp and at the same time be on the lookout for an obliging watchman filling his lamps? He was deadly. For the time being everyone was happy even though the fire was redundant but when Da heard the next day that two bags of coal were delivered to Lily White's he went berserk.

'We all know how she managed that, don't we?' Ma said.

'I don't think a Vincent man would stoop so low, Grace,' remarked Phil.

Da was all set for a night of ducking but Ma seemed a little contrite.

'Maybe we're jumping to conclusions here. Lily may have bought it from a coal merchant out of her own pocket.'

'I'll go along with that,' Phil agreed.

Da went suddenly quiet and we wondered what sort of gem he was about to come out with. He moved across and sat down at the table.

'Do you know what I'm after been thinking, Grace?'

'A beauty, I'm sure, Jack.'

'We could go to the Protestant vicar . . . '

'What's a vicar, Jack?'

'Don't be showin' your bleedin' ignorance, Grace. A vicar is the same as our parish priest and their purpose in life is to look after the needy of their parish. Now I was thinkin'. If we can manage to get a bag of coal from this vicar, then St Vincent's will have to give us one too.'

'Why would they want to give us one. I mean, they have got their own poor.'

'I know that but if Vincent's hear about it then they're bound to give us one. Don't you see? They wouldn't like the idea of us burnin' a Protestant bag of coal. What do you think?'

'And if the vicar doesn't like the idea of you burning a bag of Vincent's coal, Jack, we could end up with shag all,' Ma warned him.

'You may have to do a deal with the vicar, Jack,' said Phil.

'What sort of deal?'

'Like changing your religion.'

Ma wasn't too pleased when she heard that. 'So you want to change your religion for a bag of coal, Jack?'

'I didn't say that. I just thought that two Christian churches should help each other, that's all.'

'Jack . . . ' Advice from Phil coming up! 'When St Vincent's man comes next week pour him out a wee drop of the craythur and I'll bet you'll have a bag of coal the next day. And now I'm off to me bed. Good night all!'

6

TRUE CONFESSIONS

When Da decided we should both go to confession I knew it wasn't going to be a good day. We entered the church and Da moved to the confessional on the right, which was a mistake. I tugged at his sleeve and tried to move him away towards another box but to no avail.

'What's the matter, Charlie? Do you not like the colour of the box?'

'It's not the box, Da; it's the priest . . . '

'He's only a priest. He won't kill you.'

'He shouts and screams, Da, and everyone in the church knows what you've done.' Da shrugged his shoulders and smiled. If he had looked round he would have seen that there were very few people at our box, while a big crowd was at the box opposite.

'Listen, son: I have a clear conscience, so he won't be shouting at me.'

'He will when you tell him you lifted five Woodbines last week from Mrs Cullen's shop.'

Da was angry. 'I paid her later on when I got me labour money.'

'You still have to tell the priest you lifted them.'

'Just keep your mouth shut and don't tell your Ma about Cullen's shop.'

Da still looked angry, so I decided to change the subject.

'Did you ever go to a tough priest, Da?'

'No, I used to pick the man I wanted. I remember it was a long time before I met your Ma. There was a grand priest in the parish church where we lived.'

'Was he nice, Da?'

'Yes indeed! He was very nice, very deaf and very old. Do you know, you could tell him anything and he'd just nod his head. When you were sayin' the act of contrition you could be singin' 'Galway Bay' for all he knew. God be good to him but you won't find a gentleman like him nowadays.'

Mrs Flynn who lived down the road from us sat in the front seat and her son Tom who was in my class was about to enter the confessional. He looked so nervous I felt sorry for him. He turned to me with a sickly smile. For a minute or two there was silence. Then Fr Boyle – that was the priest's name – came into his own. 'How many times did this happen?' Everyone in the church heard him. Poor Tom! I was sure he'd have to change his trousers when he got home. Even the people at the box opposite looked across when they heard the priest shouting. He kept it up: 'Where did this happen? And take your finger away from your nose when I'm talking to you!' Poor Mrs Flynn looked around and gave Da a wan smile and I'm sure he felt sorry for her.

'He's only here for a short time, Da,' I reassured him.

'How do you know that?'

'The headmaster told us he was going back to China.'

'China! Jasus, the Chinks will boil him in rice if he shouts at them the way he shouts at us. Anyway, Charlie, I think we'll cancel the confessions for the day.' I was delighted as I had the same confession that Tom had.

Ma was having a cup of tea when we arrived back. 'Well, Jack, what did the priest have to say when you told him you were twelve months away?'

'Nothing much, Grace.' He was lying again.

'What do you mean, nothing much? He must have said something . . . All right, what penance did he give you to say?'

Da's shoulders began to shake with laughter as he gazed out the window. 'He gave me three Hail Marys, two Our Fathers and a partridge in a pear tree.'

Ma was livid, and I felt sick. 'That's not a bit funny,' she roared.

'Well Grace, I may as well own up. We didn't go to confession because the priest was leaving the box for his break when our turn came. He was goin' for a smoke and a cup of tea and I suppose he wanted to go to the toilet as well.' He looked across at me. 'Isn't that right, Charlie,' he said through clenched teeth.

'You're a rotten bastard of a liar, Jack,' Ma screamed at him. Then she turned to me. 'Never mind, Charlie, you and I will go tomorrow.' At that moment Da was scared of Ma and I was glad.

7

SIX-INCH NEEDLE

There is one particular day in my young life I shall never forget and it wasn't my eleventh birthday with the penny candle stuck in the middle of a piece of gur cake. No . . . it was the day when Da started to put on his local defence jacket.

'Where are you goin' in that thing? Has the war broken out again?' said Ma.

'I'm goin' to visit Lar Byrne in Patrick Dun's Hospital and I'm takin' Charlie with me, just for company's sake.'

'You're not takin' that child to that hospital.' Ma was upset.

'And why not, woman?'

'Because I don't want him picking up germs and that's why not!'

'For Christ's sake, the man is only in for an ingrown toenail.'

Phil knocked gently and walked in. 'Did I hear someone mention ingrown toenails, because I have one?'

Da jumped up from the table and pointed to Ma. 'That woman doesn't want me to visit Lar Byrne in hospital.'

'Oh, *you* can go but Charlie stays here!' Da was getting mad and I knew he'd be duckin' any minute.

'I don't think that would be advisable, Jack,' Phil advised him. 'You know how people talk.'

'What is there to talk about, Phil? The man is just goin' to have his nail removed. What's so mysterious about that? I met his wife yesterday and she asked me to pay him a visit. She says nobody bothers to call to see how he is.'

Ma walked across to the window. 'The poor woman. I feel sorry for her.'

Da looked stupid as he glanced at Phil, then at Ma. 'It's only a bleedin' ingrown toenail he has.' I could see he was angry.

'Then why is he in a special building at the back of the hospital?' said Ma. 'He's away from everyone you know.'

'Maybe it's a special place for removing ingrown toenails.'

'It's a special place, all right, and they remove more than toenails. A man who frequents Merrion Square lookin' for brassers is not suffering from ingrown toenails.'

'And what is he sufferin' from, then?'

'Something you don't suffer from this past few years.'

I couldn't understand some of the things Ma used to come out with but Phil seemed to. He even told me what a brasser was. 'Listen, Charlie,' he whispered, 'a brasser is a man who fits brass plates on doors, like a doctor's house or a solicitor's.' So now I knew! But how could a man who fits brass plates on doors be the cause of putting Mr Byrne into hospital? I was soon to learn. Da poured himself a cup of tea, sat down and stared at Ma.

'You don't believe Lar Byrne has an ingrown toenail, Grace, do you?'

Ma ushered me to the far end of the room and told me to study my schoolbooks. Then she sat down and looked at Phil, who nodded his head slowly. He knew something was coming. Ma folded her arms and leaned on the table.

'Jack,' she began, 'you do not get a six-inch needle stuck up . . . up into . . . into your . . . '

'Make your mind up, Grace. Does the needle go *up* or *into* something?'

'Yes, his private parts, and it's not *up*, it's *into* if you know what I mean.'

'That's right, Jack,' Phil interjected. 'You don't get an ingrown toenail when you associate with brassers.' There was that word again! I reckoned that at that moment the man fitting brass plates on doors wasn't too popular.

'How do you know all this, Phil?' asked Da.

'I heard it down at the bookie's shop; they have it on good authority there.'

'That's a great duckin' shop. They were able to tell how I was caught sleepin' on a bulldozer and how I lost my free beef voucher. Do they also give the weather forecast, by the way?'

'I never asked them that, Jack. They seem to get all the latest gossip from Lily White. She knows everything that's goin' on; you should know that, Jack.' Once Lily's name was mentioned Da didn't want to know.

'I still think I should go and see what sort of treatment

he's gettin'. After all, Grace, you never can tell when one of us could suffer from an ingrown toenail.'

'It's a dose he has,' said Ma and Phil in unison.

Da was speechless for a minute or two. 'You mean he got it from one of those brassers,' he mumbled. Ma and Phil nodded their heads together. 'And he could die from it? And all the time I thought he had an ingrown toenail.'

I didn't know what the man with the brass plates did but I didn't think that I would like him. I continued on reading my books as Ma, Da and Phil sat at the table drinking tea with a dash of whiskey that Phil had added. Suddenly there was a knock on the door which startled the three of them. Ma went across and opened it and in walked Mrs Byrne. Ma was very surprised to see her.

'Hello, Mrs Byrne. You'll have a cup of tea, won't you?'

Da stood up from the table. 'Hello, Mrs Byrne. I meant to go up to the hospital to see Lar.'

'Ah, it's just as well. Lar is gone.'

'The Lord have mercy on him.'

Byrne looked surprised. 'He's not bleedin' dead yet. They just moved him to another hospital that deals with that complaint.'

'Did the doctors tell you what his complaint was?' said Ma, as if she didn't know. She was a cute woman – deadly!

'They're not quite sure but they don't believe he fell off his bike, like he told them.'

'You could injure a certain part of your anatomy falling off a bike,' Phil assured her.

'Well you don't get his complaint fallin' off a bike.' Ma was awful.

'What complaint do you think it is, Mrs Doyle?' Mrs

Byrne wasn't too pleased but Ma was smart.

'An ingrown toenail, I believe.'

'And who, may I ask, said he had an ingrown toenail?'

'Lar told me himself a few weeks ago,' Da told her. 'I saw him myself barely able to walk. He told me he was goin' for treatment and expected to be admitted to hospital shortly.'

Da and Ma were playing it cute, and as for Phil, he didn't have to play it – he was cute.

'Well you seem to be well informed about my husband's misfortune. Did he also tell you how he came by it and what treatment he was gettin'?'

'Only that he was gettin' a six-inch needle stuck up it.' Da was brave.

'Stuck up what?'

'Wherever they stick it for people with a limp or a bad toenail or somethin'. And then maybe he finds it hard to pass water and they have to clear it.'

Things were not getting any better especially when Byrne lashed out at Da. 'It's not a fuckin' downpipe he has. He can piss as well as the next man and maybe further. And I'd like to know where you get all your information from.'

Da was looking a bit pale. He stared across at Phil. 'Phil here – he heard snatches of conversation in the bookie's shop.'

Phil wasn't too pleased with Da and Byrne certainly wasn't too pleased with Phil. 'I thought bookie's shops were used for backin' horses and not for slanderin' people. Do yis have nothin' else to do only slag people, good respectable people?'

'I'm sorry, Mrs Byrne, but it was the six-inch needle that had me worried.' Phil's cup rattled in the saucer as he spoke.

'What bleedin' needle are you talking about? I've heard nothin' but six-inch needles being mentioned since I got here.'

Ma, who had been silent for some time, looked across at Byrne. 'I'm sorry, Mrs Byrne, but it was me that first mentioned the needle. I thought he might have got something wrong with ... his private part; excuse me being so blunt.'

'I may not have any children but that doesn't mean he got it for stirring his tea, like some people I know.' Ma and Da exchanged glances while I continued to read my books.

'Well I'm sorry, Mrs Byrne,' said Ma as she left her to the door. 'And I hope everything turns out all right.'

'Oh, it will, Missus. Once the abscess on his backside is lanced he'll be fine. Thank you, and I'll see you again.'

When she was gone Phil started: 'Jack, you nearly got me in trouble with that woman!'

'Anyway, you should stay away from that bookie's shop, especially with Lily White always hanging around there. I wouldn't like to visit you in hospital and be lookin' at a six-inch needle sticking out of it.'

'I don't believe Lar Byrne has an abscess on his arse.'

Ma was cruel but Da was worse: 'No,' he said tittering. 'He probably had it on top of Old Smokey!'

'You could be right ... ' said Phil in a dream.

'About what, Phil?'

'The bookie's shop with Lily and them other cuckoos that come in.' He stood up and made for the door.

'Where are you off to now, Phil?' Ma enquired.

'I might drop into the bookie's, Grace. I might hear something interesting to pass on.'

'You should try backin' horses sometime – for a change!' advised Da.

'What? And spoil my day?'

I packed my books away. Again it was a day like every other day – you know!

8

BLESS THIS HOUSE

It was a week after my eleventh birthday when the priest, a middle-aged bald man and not too bright looking, arrived to bless our room.

'That's a fierce amount of stairs I'm after climbing,' he gasped. 'And every step creaks. I also noticed some of the banisters missing.'

'Yeah,' Da said, 'they were broken up for firewood during the emergency – no coal to be had and the turf you got was soaking wet.'

'Did *you* use any of the banisters, Mr Doyle?'

'No, Father. I'm not a destructive man.' Da could fool the best; he had the knack. Although he didn't dismantle the banisters himself, he did pick up some that happened to be lying around.

The priest looked round the room shaking his head. 'I think it's a waste of good holy water, blessing this place. It's falling down.'

'Jasus, Father, it fell down years ago! Excuse the language, Father.'

'Don't apologise, Mr Doyle. Sure I use it myself on occasions.'

'I don't think the holy water will keep the walls up ...'
(I was wondering when Ma was going to open up, and
open up she did!) '... For instance, did you see the state
of the toilets in the yard – no proper door, no slates on
the roof?'

'That's a disgrace, Mrs Doyle. What do you do if you're
having ... let me see ... a sit-down and someone happens
to come along?'

'Well, Father, they can either sit on your lap and wait
or go back and bring a chair down.' Ma was now in top
gear.

The Da started up. 'And if you take a dose of salts
you'd have to book your seat.'

'Those are disgraceful conditions to be living under.'

There was a timid knock at the door and Phil walked
in. 'Hello, Father,' he said, 'would you mind giving my
room a splash of your holy water. Not much, mind you.
The walls are already damp.'

'You're living on the same landing? Well, I've been
looking around this room and these walls go straight into
your room. So I'll bless both at the same time.'

Phil looked annoyed. 'That means if these people have
bad luck it could transfer into my room.'

'I'm sorry about that. Now will you all kneel down so
that I can get on with it.' After three Hail Marys the priest
splashed the holy water against the walls, some of it
nearly blinding Da, made the sign of the cross, put the
little bottle of water in his pocket; and then suddenly
changed the subject.

'Tell me, Mr Doyle, did you ever get that bag of coal
from the Vincent de Paul man?'

'No we did not.'

'And why not, may I ask?'

'Because he called the man a gobshite, that's why not!' Ma was off in a hack.

'What man?'

Phil edged closer to the priest and whispered. 'Michael Collins but he was shot dead in Cork before he could deliver it.' The priest stared at Phil. He was a little dim – the priest, that is, not Phil.

'So we didn't buy any coal. We were just waiting for Collins to deliver a bag.' Ma was at her best.

'Is it *the* Collins we're talkin' about?'

'The very same,' said Da with a smirk.

'He was a great man.'

'For Christ's sake don't start all over again or the holy water will go dry in your pocket and the walls come tumblin' down.' This was Ma at her best.

The priest stood up. 'I don't think I can take much more of this; besides I'm in a hurry. I've got a wedding in two hours' time and there's money to be made at weddings, you know! There's another little backhander to be made this evening when they bring the body of an unfortunate man who threw himself under a train.'

Phil was annoyed at the priest's outburst and so were Ma and Da. 'How much would it cost me for you to throw a drop of water on my walls, Father?' Phil asked sarcastically.

'And I suppose you'd like me or me wife to throw ourselves in front of a duckin' train so that you'll get another few bob?'

'What sort of a train is a duckin' train, Mr Doyle?'

Ma was quick: 'My husband doesn't mean a duckin' train, Father. What he really means is a . . . ' Da rushed over and placed his hand over her mouth. After a moment Ma poured out a cup of tea and handed it to the priest. 'You mightn't get a cup at the wedding,' she said with a bit of a smile.

The priest was about to put the cup to his mouth when he heard Lily's voice. He jumped up, spilling the tea in the process. 'Are you still up there, Father. Well don't forget to drop into me. I want you to sprinkle a drop on me.'

'That's Miss White's voice. I'd recognise it anywhere.' He sounded nervous.

'You weren't with her, Father, were you?' asked Da.

'She came up to me in the street once when I was in civvies and wanted . . . '

'What!' – Ma, Da and Phil in unison!

'A cigarette,' the priest replied.

'Oh,' said Ma and looked disappointed.

The priest moved to the door. 'I hope I don't meet that woman on the way out. She has a wicked tongue and I'll have to tread lightly on these stairs.'

'That won't be easy, Father. She's bound to hear you. The best thing you can do is to walk straight past the door and ignore her.'

'But if she wants a splash of water I can't very well ignore her, Mrs Doyle, and it might do her a world of good.'

'It would do her a bit of good if there was a drop of gin in the holy water – a sort of mixer,' Phil added with a smile.

The priest finally left, walking cautiously. Ma, Da and Phil peeped over the banister rails. The priest staggered slightly and reached out for the banister that wasn't there any more. He grabbed Ma's clothesline and everything came down on top of him.

'I hope he doesn't go out in the street with my knickers on his head,' said Ma. 'It's the only pair I have.'

I ran and joined them on the stairs but Da pushed me back into the room. The priest finally got to the front door but Lily had already heard the commotion and ran out.

'Well, if it isn't the father himself! That's a fine pair of knickers you have in your hand.' The priest threw them aside. 'Are you going to bless me little room, Father?' she enquired.

I managed to sneak out and peer through the railings where I saw the priest reaching into his pocket and producing his little bottle of water. He stood on the threshold and splashed holy water all over the place.

'Are you sure that's pure holy water, Father? It's terrible like something else.'

'It's as pure as you, my good woman.'

'Is the house safe now?'

'It has the blessing of God . . . now I must go.' And he did.

Lily walked to the centre of the hall and shouted up. 'Are you still there, Jacko? Tell your judy her knickers are down here.'

'I'm surprised you know what knickers look like, seeing that you never wear any,' Da roared down.

'Well, Jacko, the pair I have down here are all ripped; your wife must have fought well.'

'The dirty rotten bitch,' Ma shouted as she rushed down the stairs but Da caught her as she was halfway down and brought her back.

'Never mind, Grace, let her keep them.'

'I'll leave them on the floor for yeh,' Lily continued. 'When the Vincent man calls he might exchange them for a bag of coal but I doubt if they'd fit anyone. They've seen too many winters and are wore out just like your husband. He's all wind and shit.'

I thought that might do it and it did just that. Now it was Da's turn to run down the stairs with Ma and Phil after him. You know what happened: Da forgot the banisters were missing and only realised this when he put his hand on an imaginary one and over he went; luckily he landed on his feet. I know it's hard to believe but he did, and after straightening himself up he immediately went to Lily's and proceeded to kick her door down. But Lily was smart, too: when she heard Da on his way down she was also on her way, straight out the front door. Da was adamant he was going to stop where he was, so he sat on the bottom step.

'I'm goin' to wait till that village bike comes back home,' he swore.

'Jack,' said Ma, 'she won't be finished her business till well after midnight. Come on back to the room.'

'Grace is right, Jack,' pleaded Phil. 'Besides, the Vincent de Paul man is due shortly and he wouldn't be too pleased if he knew you were waitin' for the quare one.'

Da and Ma moved slowly up the stairs. Phil and I walked a bit behind them. Halfway up I tugged at Phil's sleeve.

'What business does Lily do?' I whispered.

'She sells things, Charlie.'

'After midnight?'

'Especially after midnight!'

We were only back in our room when the Vincent de Paul man called and it was the same guy! This was the man who told Da to ask Michael Collins for a bag of coal but I heard Phil say that Collins was dead. It seemed very complicated to me. The Vincent's man walked over to Ma.

'Hello, Mrs Doyle,' he said, completely ignoring Da. 'There's no need for me to look round the room', he said as he wrote in his notebook. 'You'll be getting much the same as last week,' he continued, gazing across at Da. He then turned to Phil. 'Are you living with these people?'

'No sir. I'm just the next door neighbour. I help these people as best I can.'

Now Da didn't like this one little bit. 'What did you ever do for us except give us an oul' pair of shoes to keep the fire in. You've an awful duckin' nerve.' Luckily the Vincent's man didn't know the real meaning of 'duckin'' or we would have got sweet shag all.

'Well, Jack, I did give you an odd drop of whiskey just to keep warm – seeing you have no firing and the weather so cold.'

I saw Phil wink at Da behind the Vincent man's back but Ma didn't. She exploded. 'You've an awful bloody cheek talking to Phil like that. He's been a great help to us,' she shouted.

The Vincent man looked a bit nervous as he looked from one to the other. 'I'm sorry to be the cause of all this acrimony,' he stammered. 'If there's anything I can do to help, just mention it.'

'Just give us a bag of bleedin' coal; that's all we're askin' for. It's freezin' cold up here. Do you know, we're higher than Nelson's Pillar; not a lot knows that.' I never knew that. There was a lot going on in the house that I never knew.

'I'll see what I can do next week and . . . '

'We may not be here next week!' Da was flying.

'And where will you be next week, Mr Doyle?'

'Where there's plenty of heat.'

'Where about would that be, Mr Doyle?'

'Glasnevin crematorium. You can't get any hotter than that.'

The Vincent man kept a straight face. 'Very well, Mr Doyle, you will get a bag of coal, this and every other week.'

Da was delighted; he even walked over to the man, shook his hand and left him to the door.

'Well, thank God for that!' Ma said. 'For a minute I thought you were goin' to call the man a gobshite again.'

'Ah no, Grace. He is a very nice man and I wouldn't insult him; he's a gentleman.' This time I thought it was Da that was the gobshite but he was a very smart one.

'Well, all the same, I think you still owe Phil an apology, the way you slag him off.'

'Ah no, Grace. Jack and I had it all worked out.'

'When did yis conjure up this?'

'Don't ask,' Phil told her as he left.

Well this was a good day, the last part at least; but the first part? Forget it!

9

PISSING AGAINST THE BISHOP'S DOOR

One of the blackest days in our lives happened a few days short of my twelfth birthday. Da staggered in drunk and told Ma he had been stopped by a guard and summonsed.

'And what did he summons you for, may I ask?' asked Ma not showing much sympathy.

'Pissing against the bishop's front door.'

'I see; and would no other door suit you? Could you not hold on till you got home?' Ma was really annoyed and when he told her he was to appear before a judge the next week that about tore the arse out of it. 'And where did this money come from, for the drink?'

'A man I met had just won ten pounds on the horses and he kindly invited me into O'Brien's pub for a few drinks.'

'Did you know this man?'

'He was a total stranger. He said he wanted a little company to celebrate his good fortune.'

'Was he quare?'

'What do you mean by that, Grace?'

'Yeh know fuckin' well what I mean. There's no stranger goin' to spend his money on another stranger. When he

63

feeds him with a load of beer he must expect something
at the end.'

'He was a very nice man, Grace.'

'And I think he was a fairy – you know, a handbag
man.'

'I don't know what you duckin' mean.'

'Well, let me tell you what I mean, Jack. This man
wanted to interfere with you.'

'You're well off the mark there. He was a perfect
gentleman. When we left the pub we shook hands and he
said he had enjoyed my company.'

'And did he piss up against the bishop's door too?'

'No. He went his way and I went mine.' Da moved
across to be near the table but managed to fall over a
chair in the process. Ma didn't bother to help him up. 'I'll
get meself up, Grace. I wouldn't want you to strain
yourself.' He finally made it to a chair. 'I managed that
all right.'

'You managed a lot of things tonight. First you pissed
on a man's door and then you managed to bum drinks
from a stranger.'

'I told you I couldn't hold on to it any longer and I
didn't want to do it in the open street when people were
passin' by.'

'Lily White is goin' to have a field day when she hears
this.'

'She won't know anything about it, just as long as
people are kept in the dark.'

'In a neighbourhood like this they don't know what
dark is. I'm afraid you're on your own on this trip, Jack.'

'You're not goin' to desert me in me hour of need.'

'I should have deserted you twenty years ago.'

I don't think Ma meant that. She did accompany him to the courthouse the following week and after a lot of persuasion she brought me along with her. Phil joined us later. I was thrilled to be in a genuine courthouse and having read in the newspapers accounts of cases that were heard there I was anticipating a great time. There were about twenty people in attendance, some to listen to cases that might concern them, while others came just to look and learn. When I looked across the room and saw Lily White smiling broadly I nearly shit in me pants. She gazed across at Ma but she ignored her, especially when Lily started rubbing her hands together. It was clear that she was going to enjoy the performance.

Poor Da was looking dejected as he sat alone facing the judge's throne. If he had turned and seen Lily he'd have wished to be electrocuted on the spot. After about fifteen minutes the judge, the clerks and the guards that were involved in the cases appeared. It was a guard named Drew who had charged Da. He had a big red face and looked as if he had downed a few whiskeys. He seemed very pleased with himself as he stood alongside Da.

The first case called was of a man who beat up his wife because his dinner wasn't ready when he arrived back from the labour exchange.

'You beat up your wife for such a trivial thing: your dinner wasn't ready?'

'Yes, your honour,' yer man replied.

'And if the dinner was ready, would you be kind to her?'

'It all depends, your honour.'

'Depends on what?'

'If the dinner is well cooked.'

'And if it's not?'

'Then I'll bate her up again.'

'Well, you can try the dinners in Mountjoy for the next six months. Next case.'

Now it was Da's turn. He stood up straight and faced the judge. He wasn't afraid of no bleedin' judge, he said afterwards. I noticed Ma looking sideways to where Lily sat, still rubbing her hands in anticipation.

'Well, Guard Drew,' the judge's voice boomed out. Oh no, Da wasn't afraid but I'll bet he wished he had a second pair of trousers just then. 'What have we got here?'

'I was walking my beat when I saw this man urinating up against the bishop's front door.'

'How far was he from the door, guard?'

'He was up against it and showing no shame whatsoever.'

'Could he be seen from the street?

'The noise of it alone drew my attention. For a moment I thought it was a leaking downpipe. I'm sure others must have heard it too.'

'And was he showing this thing off, do you think?'

'I don't think so your honour.'

The judge turned to Da. 'You emptied your whole kidneys against the bishop's door.' He sounded aghast and I felt sorry for Da as he looked from the judge to the guard. At last he spoke. 'I'm s-sorry, your honour,' he stuttered, 'but I wasn't thinking of any particular door to piss against. I had to get rid of it as quickly as possible.'

'The word is "urinate", Mr Doyle,' the judge corrected him.

'You can call it what you like, sir, but I still had to get rid of it.'

'Did the bishop know it was you that pis . . . urinated on his door?'

'He did the next day when the paint started to peel off, sir.'

'And did you not go back and apologise to his lordship?'

'I did, your honour, but the housemaid told me he'd gone to Uganda. She also said that the paint has been peelin' off that door for years and every Tom, Dick and Harry pisses against it since the bishop refused the use of his hall for Sunday night dances.'

'Did you dance there, Mr Doyle?'

'Yes, your honour, I did.' (Da never danced in his life.)

'I like to go to an odd dance myself, especially on Saturday nights,' the judge informed him. 'You meet àll kinds of interesting people. Tell me, is there another reason – apart from not being able to contain yourself – why you vandalised the bishop's door?'

'Yes, your honour, I miss those dances.'

'So do I, Doyle. Case dismissed.'

Da must have been the greatest liar of all time. He codded the guard and hung the judge out to dry. He was dead on. As for Ma, she was delighted and Phil was about to throw his cap in the air when he caught Guard Drew's eyes boring into him, not looking too pleased.

Lily stopped by, looked at Da and smiled. 'Well, Jacko,' she said, 'you have me to thank for getting you off today.'

'What are you shitin' about?' Ma shouted.

'The judge, of course, Missus. He caught me eye and

recognised me in an instant.'

'Everybody knows who and what you are,' snarled Da.

'Well, Jacko, that very same judge was with me two days ago and he didn't want to dance either.' She went away laughing.

Ma and Da were happy as we left the courthouse but she had the last word as we boarded the tram for home. 'I never want to go through anything like that again, Jack, so the next time you can't hold on to it, just let it run down your leg.'

I think this was a wonderful day for everyone – except the bishop.

10

First Communion

One of my biggest disasters – well, maybe not quite a disaster – happened on the day I made my first communion. I remember walking up to the altar rails and glancing across to where Ma and Da sat. I really felt great and they were smiling; they were proud too. I finally reached the rails and when the priest bent over disaster struck. The host fell out of my mouth and ended on the floor. I bent down to pick it up when the priest who was more than a little angry shouted, 'Don't touch that host or the roof will fall in on top of us.' Nowadays people are tossing it into their mouths and chewing it like gum.

Before I returned to my seat I glanced again at Ma and Da and noticed they weren't smiling any more, which was bad. I only hoped that Da didn't start duckin' in the church. After the Mass finished we all went outside where our parents were waiting. Ma handed me a bag of broken Jacobs biscuits but Da was still annoyed.

'How did you manage to let the communion fall out of your mouth?'

'It just slipped out, Da. The priest didn't place it on

my tongue; he seemed to throw it at me.'

'You wouldn't let a bar of chocolate slip out, would you?'

'All right, Jack; it's finished. It's not the end of the world,' Ma rebuked him. 'There's many a thing slipped out of your mouth.'

We eventually arrived home and after a quick cup of tea they dragged me around to our relatives to show me off – and to see how much I was going to make. Our first stop was my aunt's house, though Ma and she didn't get on very well. Her being Da's sister didn't help either. She spent a lot of her time and money in snugs, either drinking or on the lookout for a man. Any sort of man would do, as long as he bought drink. She met me with open arms.

'Hello, Charlie. You look lovely in your new suit. What's the occasion?'

'Don't be bleedin' ignorant,' said Ma. 'Can't you see he's just made his first communion!'

'Oh yes! And the only reason he's here is to collect money.'

She moved across to the old sideboard, opened her handbag and handed me fourpence. 'That's all I have on me at present.'

Ma wasn't too pleased, especially after paying eight-pence on the tram to get there. 'Is that all you can manage? I spent more than that on the tram to get here.'

'Yeh don't think I'm made of money. I could get two loaves of bread for that.'

'You were always duckin' miserable,' said Da.

'I see you're still duckin', Jack. Why don't you be a man

and say what you fuckin' mean?'

Ma caught me by the hand. 'Come on, Jack; let's get out of here.'

We left and made our way to Ma's sister where we did a lot better – two shillings better – and the neighbours were very good also. At the end of the day we threw the money on the table and Ma started to count. 'Well, Charlie, you made fifteen shillings and sixpence for your day,' she said. 'So you didn't do too badly.'

We spent the rest of the day at the zoo and when Da was out of earshot Ma pointed to a gorilla and whispered, 'That's your Da's sister.' The gorilla seemed a little agitated and kept looking round.

'Why does she keep turning her head, Ma?'

'I think she smells your Da.'

Da soon joined us. 'That gorilla seems to be lookin' for someone or something,' he said. 'By the way, Grace, how do you know it's a she?'

'Well, Jack, I don't see anything that shows it's a male. Do you?'

'I don't see anything that shows it's a female either.' And so it went on. At least the parrot was talking sensibly.

Later we had an unexpected visit from Mrs Byrne and Da and Ma were really surprised to see her after all the trouble she had caused a month before. Ma greeted her: 'Hello, Mrs Byrne; this is a surprise. Anything the matter?'

'Oh yes, Mrs Doyle, Lar is gone.'

'What hospital is he in now?' asked Da.

'He's gone completely, Mr Doyle. He's dead. I buried him two weeks ago.'

'That's proof enough . . . '

'What do yeh mean, that's proof enough! Yeh don't think I buried him alive, do yeh?' Byrne wasn't pleased.

'I don't think Jack meant anything by it; he only wanted to make sure.'

'Make sure of what, may I ask?'

'That he was dead. He thought he was gone to another hospital.'

'Well, he should have paid him a visit, like he said he would.'

'I meant to, Mrs Byrne, but it slipped me mind.' Da was nervous.

'Well he died with a lovely smile on his face,' Byrne assured them.

'He must have been glad to go,' Da said, without thinking.

'What do you mean by that?'

'He means that after all the pain he went through, his tortured body finally gave up the struggle.' Ma was saving Da's skin again.

'He wasn't strugglin', Mrs Doyle. He died in his sleep and before he went he looked me straight in the face, nodded his head and smiled the most beautiful smile.'

'He thought he'd never get away.' Da was messing things up again. 'Some people,' he continued, 'when they are on their last do unusual things.'

'Like what?' Byrne was anxious to know.

'When they imagine sometimes they see God and He smiles at them and they smile back.' Da was making things worse.

'Then you think he wasn't smilin' at me? Is that what you're sayin'?'

'Ah no, Mrs Byrne. He probably saw God in your face.'
Da was uneasy. He stood up from the table and sat down
again.

'Well, I'd be pleased with that, Mr Doyle.'

'Dyin' people act in a funny way when they're on their
last kick.'

'You talk as if he was a fuckin' footballer, Mr Doyle.'
She sighed. 'However I'll have to be movin' along.'

'By the way, Mrs Byrne,' broke in Ma, 'before you go,
what did your husband die from?'

'An enlarged something or other. The doctor had a
name for it but I don't know what it means. Anyway he's
at peace now.' With that she left.

Ma sat down beside Da. 'You always put your foot in
it, Jack. How do you think of all the things you splutter
out! "God's face in her face" – she loved that.'

'Well, Grace, I had to comfort her the best way I could.'

'I wonder what part of him became enlarged, Jack?'

'I'm not going to answer that, Grace.'

No wonder I got mixed up with all this strange talk.

11

SUSPICION

Da wasn't too pleased two days later when he had a visit from his ex- and only employer. Mr Martin banged on the door, barged in and pointed a finger at Da. 'I always had my suspicion about you, Doyle.'

'What are you talkin' about?' Da was angry.

'I'm talkin' about a fifteen-foot girder and ten bags of cement.' At that moment Phil walked in.

'Don't tell me Phil here is your witness.'

'Not him, although he could be in on it too. This witness I have is not too far from here now.'

'I hope you're not accusing me of any theft.' Now Phil was getting angry.

'You've no business bargin' in and accusin' my husband of liftin' your poxy cement.' Now it was Ma's turn. This was going to be some ding-dong.

Martin turned on Ma: 'My witness is beyond reproach, Mrs Doyle.' I never heard that word before and looking at Ma and Da I doubted if they ever heard it either.

'I don't know what you mean,' Ma said.

'He means his witness is genuine,' Phil said. He was very

smart. 'And his witness, whoever it is, is a cute arsehole.'

'What do you mean by that?' Martin wanted to know.

'The insurance company will only pay insurance when they are sure your yard was broken into and the culprits found. If they knew you were giving a backhander to someone who is prepared to perjure themselves in court, then you and your witness will be in serious trouble.'

Martin ignored Phil but pointed a finger at Da. 'When a man like that steals a loaf from Johnston Mooney's van, then he'll lift anything.'

'That loaf of bread fell off the back of the van and ended up in a pool of water. As I was drying it with me handkerchief the horse bolted down the road.'

'And you bolted up the stairs with the loaf of bread under your arm,' said Martin with a snigger. I remembered having a few slices of that loaf for my school lunch.

'When the time comes I'll have my witness and she'll ... ' He stopped suddenly.

Phil was in like a light. 'So it was a she! I bet I know where she is.'

'It's a woman all right,' Martin confessed, 'but she's not from round here.'

'She's from round here all right and she's living in the hall flat.'

'You mean Lily White. What judge is goin' to take the word of a brasser,' Da shouted.

'It all depends on the judge,' Ma says.

'What do you mean by that, Grace?'

'Well, Jack, there are some judges who are clients of these people. I remember Lily saying that all her clients were gentlemen, like doctors and solicitors and a few judges thrown in.'

'That's slander, Missus, and if you're not careful, I'll have you charged too.' Martin was angry again but Da didn't like the way he talked to Ma, so he punched him on the chin. The door flew open and Martin fell down the stairs and landed on his arse. He quickly picked himself up again and shook his fist at Da. 'If I don't get you for liftin', then I'll get you for assault, Doyle!' He ran down the rest of the stairs with Da, Ma and Phil after him. With all the commotion who should step out of her room but Lily.

'What's goin' on here?'

'I'll let you know in a fuckin' minute what's goin' on,' Ma shouted as she aimed a blow at her but Phil dragged her away.

'Don't strike a star witness, Grace!'

All this time Da was sitting on Mr Martin. 'Don't tell them anything, Lil,' Mr Martin screamed from the floor. 'I didn't pay you anything or give you a backhander to perjure yourself, Lil. You saw everything the night my girder was stolen.'

'That's impossible, Mr Martin. How could I see anything when you were on top of me? And as regards the money, I thought that was for services rendered.'

Da released Martin, who was fuming by now. As he was about to leave he glared at Da. 'I'm not finished with you yet, Doyle. I know there must be someone who knows where my material went.' He looked at Lily. 'As for you, I never want to see you again.' He opened the door and ran down the street.

Lily ran out after him and shouted, 'You know what you can do with your poxy money.' Then she ran into her room and slammed her door shut.

I'm glad to say that was the last time we saw Mr Martin, as two men were charged with the robbery. There was a third man but he was never apprehended. I walked behind Da, Ma and Phil as we made our way to our room.

'That was a great right you gave Martin, Jack,' Phil remarked, 'and you, Grace, you were about to deliver an uppercut to Lily's jaw.'

'Let's hope we don't have to go through anything like that again, Phil,' Ma said, as she linked arms with both. You'll be wondering what sort of a day it was. Well for a change it was enjoyable.

One visitor we certainly could do without was Mrs Farrell, but she called to see Ma and there was nothing we could do about it.

'I've good news for you, Mrs Doyle,' she said as she marched in.

'Oh, and what news is that?'

'Well, first of all, I must apologise for the bit of a scrap we got into on my last visit. But now I must give you the good news: I was in touch with me late husband's spirit.'

'When was this?'

'It happened last week when I went along to a new medium or spiritualist, or whatever you call them. This time it was a man and he was ever so good. Six of us sat round the table and each person had to touch the person next to us.'

'Touch them where?'

'Their fingertips, of course. Where do you think?'

Da arrived just as Farrell sat down and for a second

or two they eyeballed each other. 'I didn't expect to see you back again, Mrs Farrell, not after our last meeting. I hope we're not goin' to have another round-table conference.'

'Ah no, Mr Doyle, and I'm sorry the way things turned out the last time but I just came over to see your wife and to tell her the good news.'

'What news is that?'

'She was in touch with Jem's spirit,' Ma interjected.

'How did yis find him?'

'We didn't find him; he found me, Mr Doyle. God knows we tried hard enough three weeks ago and he didn't show up.'

'She went to a male medium and he managed to locate him – his spirit that is. Go ahead and tell him.' Ma was anxious to know.

'Well as I explained before, he had six people sitting round the table and he told us to touch each other . . . '

'Where?' enquired Da. I had heard that before.

'Around the table, Mr Doyle.'

'No. I mean whereabouts did they touch each other?'

'By the fingertips. He then extinguished all the lights except for a small candle which was lighting on the sideboard behind him. He then called out Jem's name three times and in the distance I heard this distinct sneeze. I'd know that sneeze anywhere, Mr Doyle. I called out, "Jem! It's me! Are you at peace?"'

'Did he answer you?' Ma was off; Da turned his eyes heavenwards.

'No.'

'Then how the duckin' hell did you know it was him?' cried Da.

'Because I heard his distinctive footsteps . . . '

'Spirits don't have distinctive footsteps, Ma'am. They just float around like a deflated balloon.'

'Well this was no balloon, Mr Doyle. Balloons don't sneeze.'

'And spirits do not walk with their boots on.' Da was beginning to lose the little patience he had.

Farrell turned to Ma. 'Shall I go on, Missus?' she asked, glaring at Da.

'Yes. Do carry on; you were just saying something about a sneeze.'

'Had he a cold in his head when he was dyin'?' Da enquired.

'No he hadn't a cold when he died. He did get a belt of a bleedin' tram one day in O'Connell Street some years ago and he wasn't the better of it. Since that day he always dragged his right leg after him.'

'That's a classical case of "Come leg or I'll drag yeh!"' Da was trying to be funny but Farrell ignored him.

'And it was the draggin' sound that I recognised,' she said.

'I told you before: spirits don't make noise . . . maybe a little moan or two but never noises. They just flither around and if they see someone they didn't like while they were alive then they disappear through a wall in a hurry. I think that's what happened in your case, Mrs Farrell.' Da was in great form.

'Then you think he saw me and passed on, Mr Doyle?'

'I'm afraid Jack's right, Mrs Farrell.'

Ma was delighted to get her spoke in. I realise now that Da and Ma were setting Farrell up and they succeeded for she stood up and walked to the door. 'I thought the bastard liked me when he was alive. Well he can flither round all he likes now for I'm well rid of him.'

After she left Ma and Da had a good laugh. 'I don't think we'll see that woman again for a long time, Grace.'

'I wouldn't say so, Jack. I wonder who sneezed in that house though.'

'Forget it, Grace, and go and make a pot of tea and then we'll both flither to bed.'

That wasn't a bad day although I did notice the po was full and no one seemed to bother. Ah well, I thought, the window will be busy tonight.

12

A LITTLE DIFFICULTY

On 23 December Da was admitted into hospital with a kidney infection. There would be no Santa Claus for him that year. He was not pleased as he was thinking of putting his name down for the Santa job in Clery's again. Ma and I knew he'd never get it, not after the previous year when the manager caught him wiping his nose with his beard and then bending down and kissing the children. He was lucky he didn't get a belt of a handbag from some oul' wan.

When Ma and I entered the ward on our first visit Da was sitting up peeling an orange. There were six other patients in the ward. Ma pulled over a chair; I sat on the edge of the bed.

'Who gave you the orange, Jack?'

'That honky-tonk in the end bed.'

'That was good of the man. Why do you call him a honky-tonk?'

'I don't like the way he shakes his hips when he walks and nods his head when he passes by.'

'How are you feelin' anyway?'

'How do you think I'm feelin'! Here we are two days from Christmas and I'm missing all the fun.'

'What fun is that?'

'A few drinks and a singsong.'

'You've got no money for drink, Jack, and you couldn't sing your way out of a paper bag.'

A nurse came over with a little black box. 'I'm going to take your blood pressure, Mr Doyle.' She strapped on a belt and pressed the little rubber ball. It was all over in a few minutes.

'Excuse me, Nurse, before you go. Did someone die about three o'clock this morning?'

'That was Mr Kelly. He died about that time.'

'Why were you rushin' him down the hall so fast?'

'We had one to pick up in the next ward.'

'What was the hurry? The corpse wasn't goin' anywhere!'

'Union rules, Mr Doyle. Get rid of them quick – no overtime, you see.'

'How many did yis get rid of this week?'

'Six,' the nurse replied, and left.

'That's not good news, Jack,' said Ma. 'We'll have to be talkin' about insurance at that rate, just as a precaution, you understand.'

'What are you talkin' about, Grace?'

'Well, two went today and it's early in the week yet. Don't forget, Jack, your policy is only worth fifty pounds.'

'Fifty pounds! That wouldn't get me down the bleedin' stairs.'

'Well, we could put you on a raft, as they do in India, and give you a push off down the Liffey. With a bit of luck you could be picked up in the Irish Sea by a fishing boat, or maybe the Mail, and they might bury you at sea and I'd be fifty pounds to the good.'

'You're terrible funny, Grace. Don't forget: you could be on your way first.' A nurse came across and gave Da two tablets.

As she walked away he pointed after her. 'Do you see that nurse, Grace? Well she came to me this morning and said she wanted a urine specimen. She gave me this gadget to piss into but the neck of it was very narrow. I had trouble gettin' me . . . ' He leaned over and whispered into Ma's ear.

'You always had trouble gettin' it in, Jack.' They were talking in riddles again.

'This is a narrow-necked bottle I'm talkin' about, and to make things worse the nurse stood next to me and looked at me strugglin'.'

'With what? The bottle or the other thing?'

'I'll ignore that. I was thinking of askin' the doctor to release me for Christmas Day.'

'I don't think that would be a good idea, Jack.'

'Why not?'

'Well, you're sure of a Christmas dinner here.'

'Don't tell me you have duck all in the house.'

'We have enough for me and Charlie; you won't be lonely with all the other patients . . . What are they like anyway?'

'I'm surrounded by six gobshites. Do you see that old man opposite? Well, he talks to St Francis every night.' Ma and Da were talking so much that they never noticed the old man moving towards them but I did.

'Excuse me, Mr Doyle. May I sit down for a minute or two?' He didn't wait for an invitation. He looked at Ma. 'Is this your wife?'

Da sat with folded arms and stared at him. 'Never you mind who she is. What do you want?'

'It's about St Francis.'

'What about him?'

'He gave me some disturbing news last night.' Da looked at Ma.

'Hold on to your scapular, Grace. Here it comes. What was the disturbing news?'

'He told me there would be an empty bed tomorrow.'

'Is there somebody bein' discharged?'

'No, Mr Doyle. We'll all be in our beds tomorrow but one will be stiff. St Francis is never wrong; even the little birds that flock around him know something.'

'Lily White wasn't one of those birds, was she?'

'Jack, don't talk like that!' Ma was very serious.

'Well, he has the shite frightened out of everyone in the ward.'

'But suppose he's right?' Ma was about to put the kibosh on things. 'He *could* be talkin' to St Francis.'

'Don't tell me you're fallin' for that, Grace.'

The old man went back to his bed with a smile on his face while Ma continued. 'Well, suppose I came to visit you tomorrow and found your bed empty, what would I think?'

'Would it never occur to you that I might be in the toilet havin' a sit-down or maybe doin' a rhumba with the matron?'

'You could be fuckin' dead too.'

The old man was makin' his way across again but Da was really mad. He threw off the bedclothes and jumped out but then calamity! It seems that the elastic on his pyjamas was weak and down the pants fell round his ankles. He stood semi-naked in the middle of the floor. Ma and I could do nothing but laugh, while the old man stared up and down at Da. 'I don't know how you struggled to get that thing into a bottle; it should fit a keyhole.' A nurse ran over and put a safety-pin in the bottoms and told him to get back into bed. Da was mad and the old man's laughing at him didn't help.

'St Francis will have a good laugh when I tell him what happened here today,' the old man shouted over.

But St Francis was right about an empty bed: the old man died during the night.

'I'm not sorry to see that oul' fella go. He was about gettin' on me bleedin' nerves.' Da didn't seem to regret the old man's death at all.

On our second visit Phil came with us. Da was still unrepentant about the old man. 'I don't think you should talk about the dead that way, Jack,' said Ma. 'The poor man wasn't all in it.'

'He was right about an empty bed, though. I bet he didn't think it would be *his* bed. Francie fooled him; now we have a redundant bed and God knows what gobshite we're going to get.'

'How are you feelin' now, Jack?' Phil asked.

'A little better since that old man departed from us.'

'I believe you had a little bother with a bottle when you were asked to give a urine sample.' Again Da looked angry – but when was he ever any other way?

'And who told you that, Phil? Don't tell me you heard it at the bookie's.'

'No, it seems some of the doctors here are clients of you-know-who.'

'Yeh mean Lily White?' Da got in quickly.

'The very one, Jack. She was able to tell me you had a little difficulty gettin' something into the bottle.'

'It was a narrow-necked bottle, Phil,' said Ma, hoping to keep the peace. 'And the nurse lookin' on didn't help.'

'Well, of course, you're bound to get nervous when you have someone lookin' over your shoulder.'

'Are you two finished talkin' about me?' Da enquired.

'I was just explainin' things to Phil, Jack.'

'The old man you were tellin' me about, Jack – he could be a saint. It's not everyone that saints appear to, you know. All these saints stick together. Was there any birds twitterin' around him . . . the old man I mean?'

'How the hell do I know? Nobody else saw him except that old man who just passed on. Anyway he was a nutcase and he should never have been allowed into a ward with sane people.' Ma looked heavenwards.

'I saw a corpse being wheeled out on a trolley, as I was on my way in,' said Phil.

'That happens very often in this place; people are dying to get out of the kip.'

'When is your next urine test?' Ma couldn't resist it.

'How do I bleedin' know? I'm not a doctor, yeh know.' Da was still angry.

'They say after they get the result of the second test they'll either let you home or hold on to you for a little while longer,' Phil said.

Then Ma started up; and how she could start up! 'And if yeh still can't get it in, they'll probably give you a milk bottle. God knows that should do!'

'I may not have to have another urine test, woman. Now with the old man and St Francis gone I feel a lot better.'

Da was released on 26 December and Phil paid for a cab but the horse stopped halfway up a hill. Some men diggin' up the road shouted at the cabby, 'Put a hot-water jar on his belly.' They had a good laugh to themselves.

'Put one on your sister's belly,' the cabby roared back. However the workmen gave the old horse some of their lunch and with a final push we started off again. Ma and Phil helped Da up the stairs and I was praying that Lily wouldn't show her face. But when we were halfway up, she did!

'I believe you had a little bother with a bottle, Jacko,' she shouted, 'and even St Francis couldn't help you! Maybe your wife will help straighten it out.' That was all that was needed to send Ma racing down the stairs and catching Lily as she was about to go back into her room. Ma was small but she was tough. She caught Lily by the hair and smashed her against the wall. She thumped her a few times in the face before finally pushing her back into the room. While all this was going on Phil and Da were sitting quite calmly on the stairs. I think they knew what the result was going to be. All the other tenants also knew; they applauded Ma as she made her way back upstairs.

'Are you all right, Ma?' I asked.

'I am, Charlie. Now go on inside the three of yis.' She turned to go down the stairs again.

'Where are you goin, Grace?' Da was anxious.

'I'm goin' back down to finish the fuckin' job while I'm in top gear. I'll get rid of this brasser once and for all from this house.'

I do not know if Lily heard her or not but she fled the flat and wasn't seen again. It's funny but I liked Lily. She was the only woman who kissed me on the cheek and handed me three shillings when I made the first communion. 'Don't tell your parents I gave you that and spend it wisely, Charlie.' She also patted me on the head. To me Lily was a lady and I did spend it wisely. I held on to a few coppers, though, and lit a candle at the statue of St Francis. Just for Lily.

13

Chat on the Stairs

Three days after my fifteenth birthday we had a visit from
the rent collector, who also happened to be the landlord.
Ma had bought me a new pair of shoes so I couldn't see
where the rent money was coming from. He had the ability
to appear from nowhere and catch us by surprise. His
method was crude but effective. I had just reached the
top of the stairs and was about to enter our room when I
got a push in the back that landed me on my face in the
middle of the floor.

'Don't throw your duckin' weight about here,' Da
warned him as he picked me up.

'You are three weeks overdue with the rent, Mr Doyle.'

'And next week, with the help of God, we'll be four
weeks overdue, Mr Brown.'

'My name is Green and not Brown.'

'Jack always gets his colours mixed, Mr Green, but if
you come back next week we'll have your money for you.'
Ma was being nice and that was bad.

'I have no intention of waiting another week. I want
my thirty shillings now.'

'Well, I'm afraid we haven't got it, Mr . . . whatever colour you are.'

'Green is the name, Missus, as you well know, and it's a name I won't let you forget.'

The landlord was asking for trouble; this was Ma's territory he was moving into. She jumped up from the table. 'When I say I have no money to pay the rent, I mean it', she told him.

'Well then, I'll go to the city council or even the police and get the sheriff to evict you all.'

'Well, off yeh go and get the sheriff and he can get Sitting fuckin' Bull if he wants to. They'll not shift us.'

Then Da got going. 'They can even bring along John bleedin' Wayne if they want to; they will not shift this family.'

'Look, Mr Green. We'll pay an extra two shillings a week until we have the book clear.' Ma was being nice, and I hated that.

'I don't want to be paid in that manner. What I want from you is thirty shillings or out you go. I have another tenant waiting to move in here.'

'Then they'll have a long fuckin' wait. Do you know that this must be the worst tenement in the city. I have a good mind to report you to the sanitary people over the condition of them toilets and the banisters are missing halfway down.'

At this point Da moved in again. 'Only last week a man on the second floor nearly fell to his death.'

'What happened?' Green asked.

'Mr Kelly on the second landin' was on his way down when he slipped and made a grab for the banisters that wasn't there any more and he went over the top. He was a very lucky man that an old woman was on her way up and she broke his fall. Now, Mr Green, about these toilets ... ?'

'What about them?'

'Well, a body can't have a proper sit-down without some oul' wan peeping in and telling you to hurry, and that she was bursting to let loose. It happened on numerous occasions when I had to leave the toilet with me trousers round me ankles, just to oblige someone doing a jig outside.'

'I agree with me husband.' Of course she would. 'We should have a toilet on the second floor and save people, who are three storeys up, the long journey down to the yard. Then we wouldn't have to feck the contents of the po out of the window.'

'That's a disgusting habit, Missus.' Green wasn't pleased.

'It's better than trying to balance a full po down three flights of stairs. If you happen to slip, some unfortunate person on the way up could get the full contents in the face. I don't think they'd be a bit happy, especially if they were on their way to a dance.'

'How many tenants have this filthy habit?'

'Two or three. We often meet on the stairs and have a bit of a chat.'

'With a full pot of urine?'

'Yes and some other matter, if yeh know what I mean.'

'How long is this being goin' on?'

'We've only been doin' it lately.'

'How lately?'

'About three years. At first we enjoyed our little chats but when one of the women got interfered with ... '

'What do you mean ... interfered with?' Green was hooked.

'A man got over the back wall – by the way the wall's nearly gone – and tried to put his hand on her person.'

'What was he after?'

Ma looked at Da. 'You tell him, Jack.'

'It's simple, Mr Green. He was going to molest her. You know ... accost her illegally. He was looking for something and it wasn't money.'

'Maybe the man was hungry.'

'He didn't ask for a cut of bread, sir. Anyway, we decided to stop seeing each other as it has become too dangerous, especially in these dark nights. So we all agree that the open window was the safest way to get rid of what we had.'

Green looked across at Da. 'Surely a grown man like yourself isn't afraid of the dark. What's to stop you running down three flights of stairs?'

'Why should I? All I've got to do is stand in front of the window with a bicycle tube.' Ma and Da were really working Green up and you can bet that they were being successful.

'I've never in all my life heard such filth, but don't forget if I don't get four week's rent next week, you are all out on your ears and when the sheriff hears all about your dirty habits, nothing can save youse.'

'I hope the sheriff has a posse with him,' Da shouted after him. Ma and Da were a great team and I loved listening to them. When they got going they would put the frighteners on anyone. Don't ask me what sort of day it was ... please!

14

LONG AGO AND FAR AWAY

It was a sad day when Da heard his sister was admitted to a mental hospital. He decided to take me with him on his first visit, just for company's sake. He always wanted me with him when he was afraid to go places alone. Ma didn't like the idea.

'You can't take Charlie to a place like that.'

'And what's wrong with a place like that?'

'Well he's goin' to see some strange people – people he didn't know existed before.'

'That's the trouble, Grace. There's many walkin' the streets of this country who don't give a damn about these people. Do you know: some of these patients are in a home for years and their relatives don't want to know. They don't want to know because they put them away themselves.'

'What do you mean, Jack: their relations don't want to know? Surely they must visit them sometimes and bring them cigarettes or something?'

'They don't visit them because they do not want them and in some cases they are ashamed of them.'

'I don't believe that, Jack.'

'Well, you can believe it. Now I'm goin' to visit my sister and Charlie is coming with me.'

We left and soon boarded a tram where we had a little bit of bother. Da handed the conductor threepence, two for him and one for me. The conductor looked at Da, then me. 'The fare is fourpence, two for you and two for him.'

'He's only twelve years of age.' I was thirteen.

'He's a hairy-looking twelve! However, I'll let you go this time. I'll remember you the next time you get on my tram.'

Da wouldn't let it go. 'Well, accordin' to the papers, in a year or two there'll be feck-all trams. It's goin' to be all buses and you might end up alongside me signing on at hatch twenty-one. We'll see how bleedin' cocky you are then!' We finally reached our destination.

'Remember what I told you,' the conductor shouted as the tram moved off. 'Duck you and your tram,' Da called after him.

We entered the hospital grounds through big iron gates and Da went across to a man in a wooden office. 'Excuse me, sir. I'm lookin' for the women's part.'

'Straight down and the third building on the right.' We started to walk and on our way we met a man in a wrinkled grey suit who seemed to have lost something in the long grass.

'Are you lookin' for somethin'?' Da enquired.

The man looked up and gave us a toothless smile. 'I've lost a button. It was a lovely brass button.'

Da believed him but the man in the dark blue uniform who seemed to have sneaked up on us didn't.

'Is he lookin' for a button?' he asked Da.

'Yes, sir, a brass one.'

'He's lookin' for that fuckin' button for the past twenty years.'

'Well, I think you should show the man some respect,' said Da as we continued on our way. He held me tightly by the hand, a sure sign he was a bit nervous, and the man shouting through the iron bars did not help. 'Hey you, come over here. I want to talk to you,' the man shouted but we kept on walking. On our way we saw a lovely bowling green and we stopped for a moment to watch some women playing. A nurse was passing and Da stopped her to say, 'Isn't it grand to see those patients enjoying themselves!'

'They're not patients; they're nurses and doctors.'

'And is there no place for patients to partake in these games?'

'If they feel like it they can but they're not a bit interested,' said the nurse, and went on her way.

We eventually found the building and went in through a big front door. Inside two nurses sat behind a table. Da approached them and enquired about his sister. They pointed towards the end of the room, a room that was long and wide with patients sitting on both sides. I noticed one old woman pushing a brush in front of her. There was a cloth wrapped round the brush to make a sort of polisher. She never once stopped as she pushed the brush up and down, her eyes never leaving the floor. Some of the women gave us a sort of smile and one old woman came up to me and handed me a hard crust wrapped in a piece of cloth, before running back to her seat when she saw a nurse approaching.

'Could I bring my sister out for a bit of fresh air?' Da asked but the nurse refused. He sat down beside my aunt and held her hand. 'Hello, Pat. How are you today?' She never answered but just stared ahead. 'This is Charlie, your nephew. He came specially to see you.'

She completely ignored us; we might have been on another planet for all she cared. The woman with the brush was still walking up and down polishing that damned floor. A woman opposite started a fight with another patient. They screamed at each other but the nurses soon put a stop to it. Da put his arm round Pat's shoulder but she shrugged it away. Then she started to rock herself to and fro, keeping her hands tightly clasped together. She began to sing 'If I Were a Blackbird' and a woman a few yards up shouted, 'Don't start singing that feckin' song again.'

'Pat, listen to me, please. We are the only two left in our family. Our parents are both gone; Sean and Alice, the brother and sister, are both dead and you and I are the only ones left.' For the first time in my life I saw Da cry.

Pat suddenly stopped rocking and looked him straight in the eyes. 'I want you to go, Jack, and don't ever bring that child here again,' she said quietly. Then she turned to me, bent over and whispered, 'Charlie, kiss me on the cheek and pray for me. That is all I ask.' As I leaned over she squeezed my hand and I kissed her. I looked at Da and felt so sorry for him as he wiped his eyes. As he stood up Pat grabbed him by the arm. 'Jack, don't ever come back to this place again.'

'Don't be silly, Pat. I'll be here next week.'

'I may not be. The doctor told me three days ago my

liver's already destroyed. I suppose I did drink myself to death.'

'I'll see you next week,' said Da as he bent down to kiss her. Then we walked slowly to the door. As it closed I looked back. My aunt was rocking again and the old lady was still pushing her polisher up and down. I cried. The following week my aunt was dead.

1955 was a sad year for me. I had just finished my training when Ma died. I was glad that she had lived to see me settled. Phil died four years before Ma, and Lily, God rest her, was killed in a traffic accident. Da eventually got casual work at the docks but the harsh winters on the quays took their toll and he died of tuberculosis. At the close of each day, and in the stillness of the night, I pray for my parents, and for Phil, Lily and all my friends. During my prayers – and I hope I am forgiven for it – a thought intrudes: did Da help load the cement and that girder on to the lorry? I do remember him brushing his waistcoat vigorously when he came home that morning. 'It's only flour, son. It must have blown from Boland's mill up the road. Now off you go to school.' At the time I never knew what colour cement was. Now I know, and it wasn't white.